Farshore

First published in Great Britain 2021 by Farshore
An imprint of HarperCollins*Publishers*
1 London Bridge Street, London SE1 9GF
www.farshore.co.uk

HarperCollins*Publishers*
1st Floor, Watermarque Building,
Ringsend Road Dublin 4, Ireland

Written by Katrina Pallant
Designed by Jeannette OToole

© 2021 Disney Enterprises, Inc.
Pixar properties © Disney/Pixar
The movie THE PRINCESS AND THE FROG copyright © 2009, Disney, inspired in part by the book
THE FROG PRINCE by E. D. Baker copyright © 2002, published by Bloomsbury Publishing, Inc.
Based on the book THE HUNDRED AND ONE DALMATIANS
by DODIE SMITH. Published by William Heinemann Ltd.
© POOF-Slinky, LLC

ISBN 978 0 7555 0110 6
Printed in Italy
001

A CIP catalogue record for this title is available from the British Library.

Parental guidance is advised for all craft and colouring activities. Always ask an adult to help
when using glue, paint and scissors. Wear protective clothing and cover surfaces to avoid staining.

Stay safe online. Farshore is not responsible for content hosted by third parties.

Farshore takes its responsibility to the planet and its inhabitants very seriously.
We aim to use papers from well-managed forests run by responsible suppliers.

This
Disney
Christmas
Annual 2022
belongs to

....

....

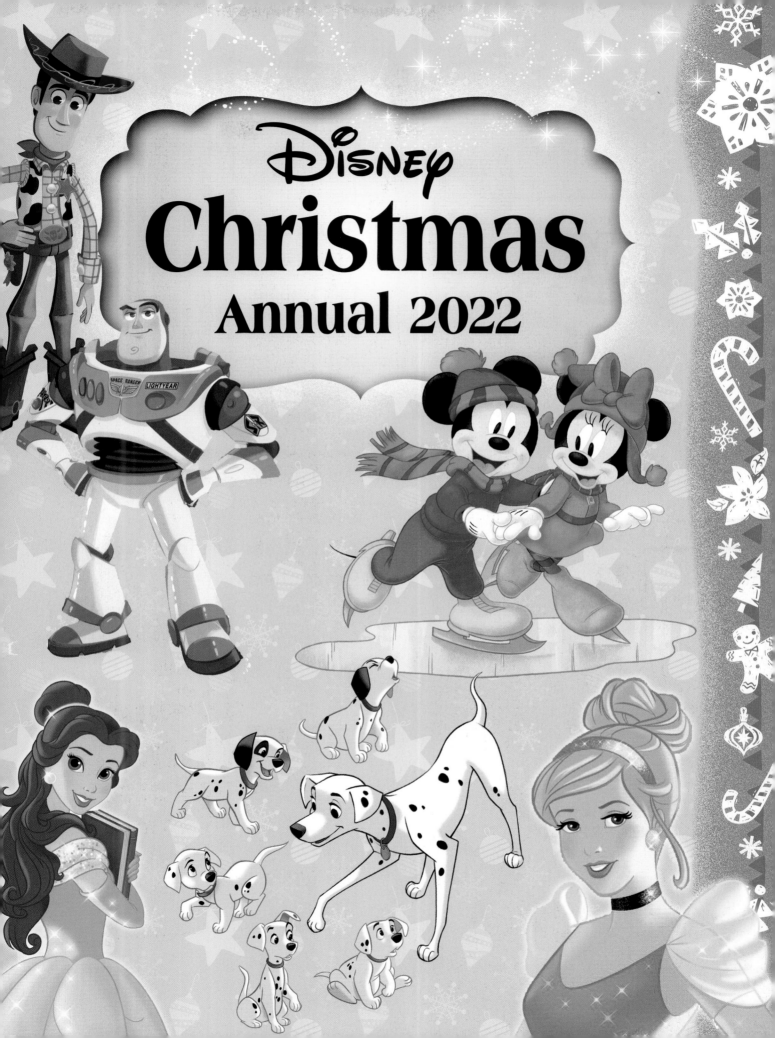

Disney
Christmas
Annual 2022

Contents

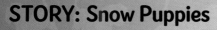

7

A New Friend

Listen to the story about a cheeky present. When you see a picture, join in and say the word!

Andy   Rex   presents   Hamm

Christmas tree   Woody   Buzz   cake

It was Christmas Eve, and while and his family were out for the

day and the gang decided to go and investigate the

around the .

"I hope one of the new toys is a dinosaur friend for me!" said ,

as he ran around looking for familiar shapes.

"Careful, everyone," said. "We don't want to make a mess or

disturb any of 's new toys."

Then  noticed some ripped wrapping paper on the floor.

"Oh no!" he cried. "A new toy has escaped! We need to find it before

 and his family get home."

The gang searched high and low for the new toy. looked

behind the sofa. looked in the fridge. looked under the

bed. But the new toy was nowhere to be seen.

Finally, found a teddy bear covered in tinsel in the kitchen,

trying to eat the Christmas .

"Come on now, friend," said gently. "We need to get you back

in your wrapping paper before gets home."

The gang rushed to wrap the teddy bear back up just as a car pulled

into the driveway.

"Phew!" said as the toys quickly returned to 's

bedroom. "That was close."

"Yes," said . "No sign of any dinosaurs, but at least we get a

new friend who loves Christmas as much as we do!"

Which Path, Woody?

Which path leads Woody to his Christmas present from his friends?

ANSWER: Path c leads to the present.

Gift Doodle

What would your ideal present be for Christmas this year? Draw it here.

Pal's Puzzle

These two pals are telling Christmas tales.
Find the missing piece of this picture below.

ANSWER: Piece 2 is the missing piece.

Count and Colour

The toys were getting ready for the big day.
Count the stockings then colour them in!

Santa Spelling

Bonnie is writing her letter to Santa to tell him what she'd like for Christmas this year. Help her out by tracing the missing words.

Dear Santa,
I would like some new
toys
please.
love from
Bonnie

Toy Shadows

Match up Bonnie's toy friends with their shadows.

ANSWER: 1-c, 2-b, 3-d, 4-a.

A Christmas Gift for Chip

It was Christmas Eve at the castle. Chip was asleep in his cupboard and Belle was looking for something to help him have the best Christmas yet. She found a perfect set of toy carriages in the Beast's childhood bedroom.

"How dare you enter here!" Beast shouted. Belle was afraid and took refuge in the kitchen.

"Is he always that angry?" Belle asked the enchanted objects.

Mrs Potts tried to explain.
"The master lost his favourite
toy from his mother - a white
horse with blue eyes and a black
mane. Out of sadness and anger,
he closed up that room and his
heart forever."

Belle felt sorry for the Beast, but decided to stick with her plan. When the enchanted objects went to sleep, she returned to the Beast's old room to work on the toy carriages for Chip. She lined them up and tied them together with string. Then she took the winding mechanism from a music box and put it in the first carriage.

Now all she needed to do was decorate the carriages for Chip. She found some ribbon in a drawer, but what was that behind it? The Beast's lost horse!

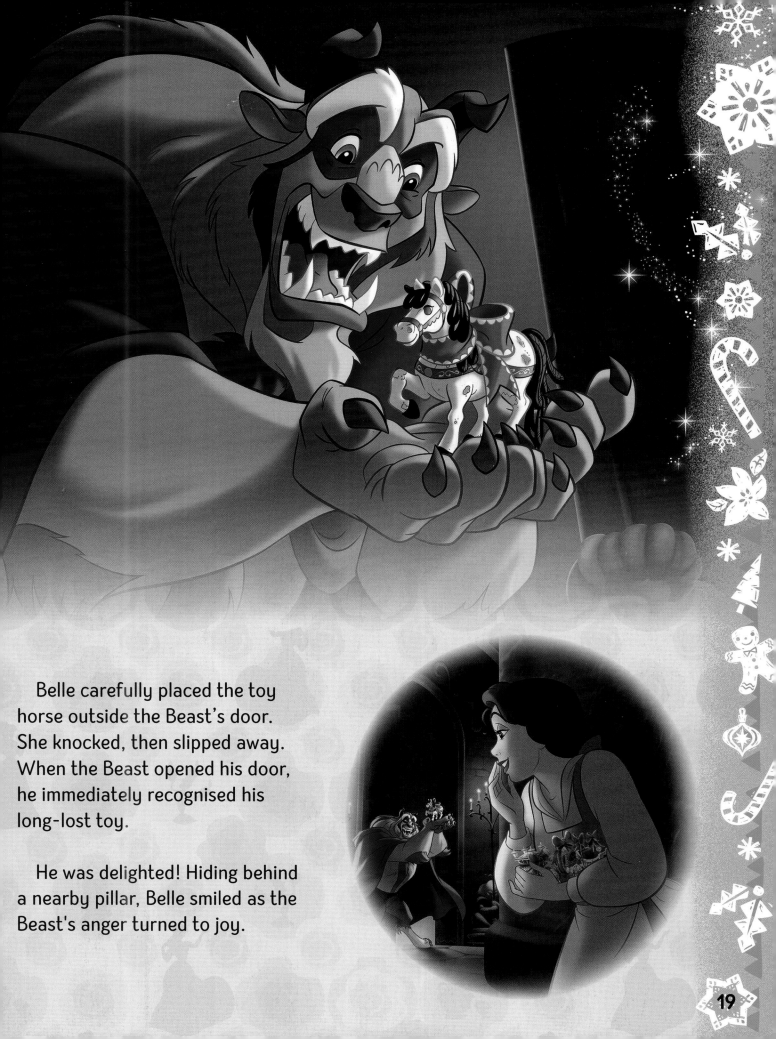

Belle carefully placed the toy horse outside the Beast's door. She knocked, then slipped away. When the Beast opened his door, he immediately recognised his long-lost toy.

He was delighted! Hiding behind a nearby pillar, Belle smiled as the Beast's anger turned to joy.

19

The next morning was Christmas Day
and Belle gave Chip his gift.
"Thank you!" smiled Chip delightedly.
Belle then flipped the switch on the
winding mechanism in the first carriage.
Chip gasped as the carriages drove off
by themselves ... as if by magic!

"I'm sorry I was cross yesterday," the Beast said.
"This horse is very special to me, so it needs someone
special to look after it," he said, passing it to Chip.
"I'd be honoured," Chip replied. Mrs. Potts wiped a
tear from her eye and Belle's heart swelled. It was the
happiest Christmas that anyone could remember.

Paper Chains

Belle loves Christmas, especially all the festive decorations. Make these paper chains with an adult to decorate your room!

Instructions

Cut out the paper strips – make some more with your own paper and pens.

Take one strip and curl it around in a circle and glue the two ends together.

Feed your next strip through the middle of the first, curl round and glue the two ends together.

Repeat until you have linked all the strips and then hang your finished festive paper chain.

© Disney
© Disney
© Disney
© Disney
© Disney
© Disney
© Disney
© Disney
© Disney
© Disney

Odd Candle Out

Lumiere is helping decorate the castle for Christmas. Which picture of the candelabra is the odd one out?

1

2

3

4

ANSWER: Picture 3 is the odd one out.

Christmas at the Castle

Chip thinks this might be the best Christmas the castle has ever seen!

Snowy Skating

The Beast is finally getting the hang of ice skating without skates!

Santa's Little Helper

It was Christmas Eve, and Mickey and Pluto were fast asleep. All of a sudden, they were woken up by a chorus of sneezes!

Outside, they found Santa Claus with some sad-looking reindeer. They all had colds and couldn't deliver the rest of the presents.

"We can deliver them!" Mickey said.

Santa gave Mickey a list of presents to deliver.

"Come on, Pluto, let's finish Santa's deliveries!" Mickey said, as they climbed on his sled.

Pluto grabbed hold of the sled's rope as Mickey held the presents. With Santa's magic, the sled rose into the air. They held on tight, as the sled took them to their first stop.

The first delivery was for Daisy. Mickey filled her stocking and ate the treat she'd left for Santa. At Goofy's house, Pluto wanted a treat too. But he knocked over the Christmas tree as he dashed to the plate of cookies.

"Maybe he'll be so excited about his gifts that he won't notice the tree," Mickey said hopefully.

Mickey and Pluto had spent so much time fixing Goofy's tree, that they didn't have long left to deliver the other presents.

They quickly delivered Minnie's gifts, then rushed to Donald's house.

But then Mickey realised that one of Donald's presents was missing. He looked everywhere, but couldn't find it!

Just then Mickey heard footsteps – Donald was awake! He grabbed Santa's sack and rushed up the chimney.

"Phew, that was way too close!" he said, as he and Pluto flew home.

29

On Christmas Day, the friends had breakfast with Mickey.

"Santa was a little out of sorts last night," said Goofy. "I think he bumped into my tree; it looked a little lopsided this morning."

"He woke me up with all the noise he made," Donald exclaimed.

"And he left one of your presents at my house," Minnie said to Donald, as she gave it to him.

Mickey winked at Pluto as he said, "Santa Claus definitely wasn't himself last night. Merry Christmas, everybody!"

Questions About the Story

Now you have read this festive story, see if you can answer the following questions.

1

What woke Mickey on Christmas Eve?

a a loud bang

b a chorus of sneezes

c a gust of wind

2

Who offered to help Santa?

a Mickey and Minnie

b Goofy and Daisy

c Mickey and Pluto

3

What did Santa hand to Mickey?

a list of presents

b a snowball

c his red hat

4

Whose tree was knocked over by Pluto?

a Daisy

b Goofy

c Minnie

5

Who had Donald's missing present?

a Goofy

b Daisy

c Minnie

ANSWER: 1. b, 2. c, 3. a, 4. b, 5. c

Pluto Loves Presents

Mickey and his friends are getting things ready for Christmas Day, but Pluto doesn't look like he can wait! Find five differences between these two festive pictures.

Colour in a star every time you find a difference.

Hurry Home!

Mickey is racing home to help decorate the Christmas tree. Help him through the maze.

34

Trim the Tree

Now it's time to decorate
your own tree.
Draw baubles, tinsel and
add a star on top, then
colour in your tree.

35

A Perfect Party

Cinderella spent all day decorating the palace for a grand Christmas ball. She wouldn't let any of the palace staff help her.

The housekeeper was surprised to see Cinderella sewing. "Why don't you ask the royal seamstresses to do that?" she asked.

"I'm making presents for our guests," Cinderella said. "It's more personal if I do it myself."

She even gathered all the food for the party instead of letting the royal chef cook! Outside, Cinderella laid out a picnic celebration for her closest friends.

Suddenly, her fairy godmother appeared. "My dear, you need a centrepiece," she said. Waving her magic wand, she turned a water jug into an ice sculpture!

"Now everything is perfect!" Cinderella exclaimed.

While Cinderella changed her gown, her fairy godmother slipped into the banquet room.

"This will never do for a royal ball," she said, looking at the decorations that Cinderella and the mice had hung.

As she waved her magic wand, an elaborate feast appeared. She waved it again and the court musicians arrived and started playing.

"But where are your guests?" the housekeeper asked Cinderella "This is a Christmas party for the royal staff, in honour of all they do," Cinderella replied.

"What a wonderful surprise," the housekeeper exclaimed.

Before long, the palace was full of the sounds of the staff enjoying the feast and music.

Leaving the staff to their ball, Cinderella went outside to greet her other guests. "Merry Christmas!" she cried.

A chorus of chirps, barks and whinnies answered. All her animal friends had come to her party!

Later, the Prince and Cinderella danced under the stars. It was the merriest Christmas celebration the kingdom had ever seen!

Pawsome Pairs

All the animals around the castle are excited for Christmas. Match up each pet to its double.

Festive Friends

Gus helps Cinderella decorate the palace tree.

Party Time

Cinderella and the Prince host a holiday ball.

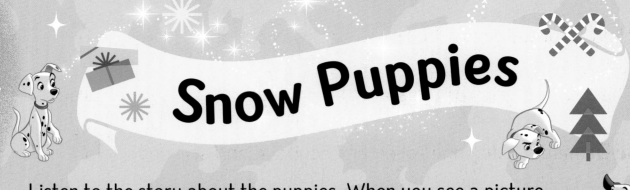

Snow Puppies

Listen to the story about the puppies. When you see a picture, join in and say the word!

puppies **tree** **presents** **snow** **present** **bed**

The were confused. Roger had brought a into the house and hung sparkly balls on it. Now Nanny was putting some boxes with bows beneath the . "What is she doing?" asked Patch. "Humans give at Christmas to show they care," Perdita said.

The decided they should give their humans a gift, so Rolly ran off and fetched his best bone. "Humans don't chew bones, silly," Lucky laughed. On their afternoon walk, the saw a group of children playing in the . This gave Lucky an idea.

When they returned home, Lucky began digging a puppy shape in the snow. The 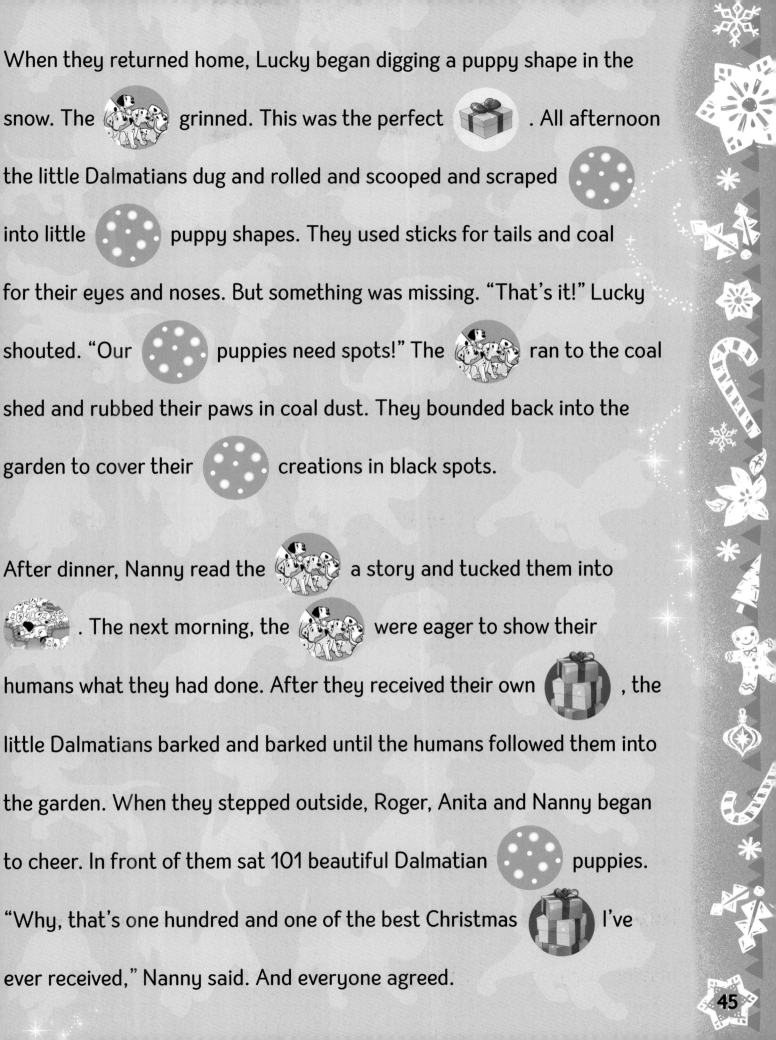 grinned. This was the perfect 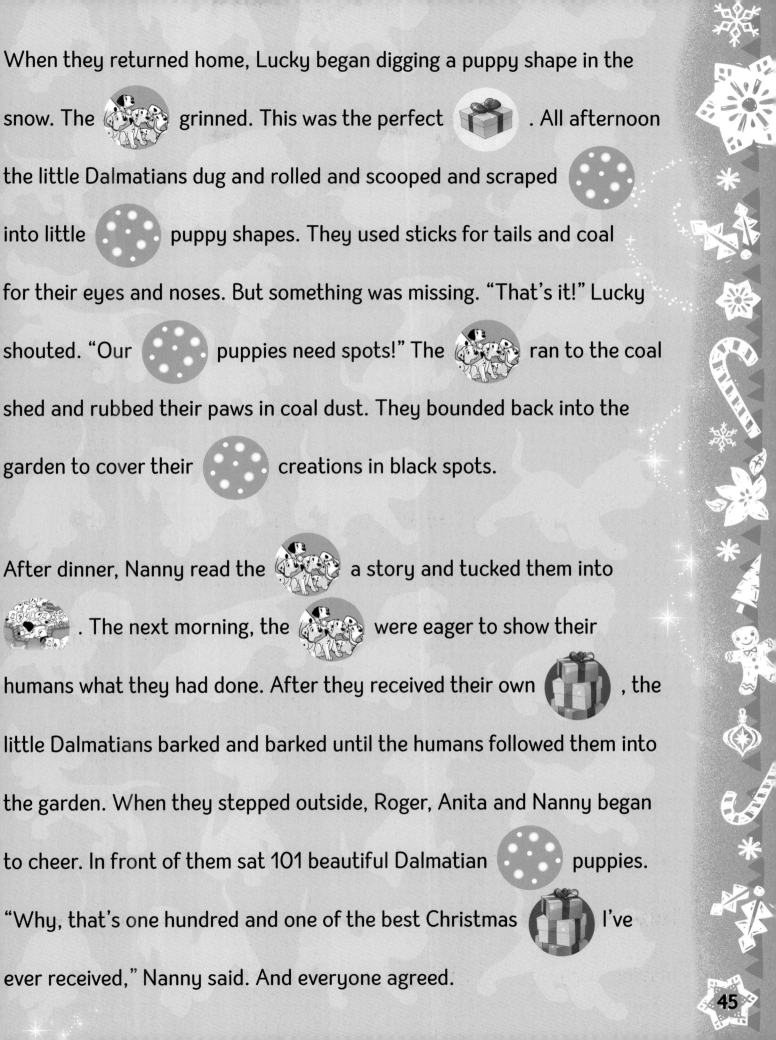 . All afternoon the little Dalmatians dug and rolled and scooped and scraped into little 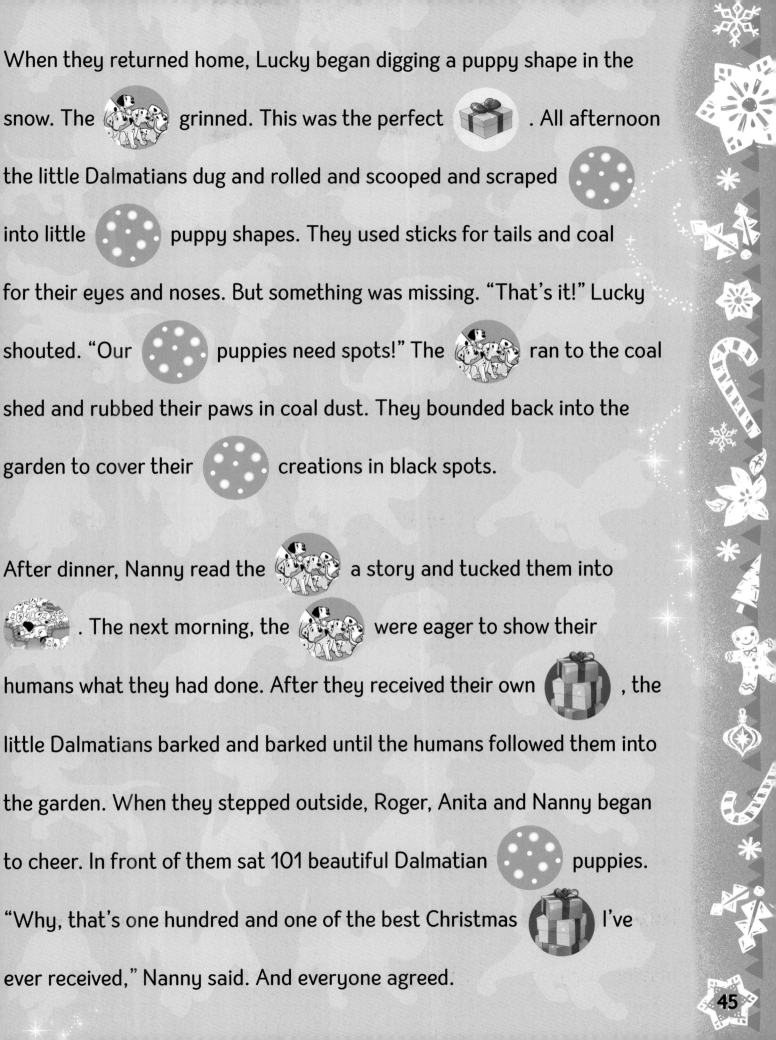 puppy shapes. They used sticks for tails and coal for their eyes and noses. But something was missing. "That's it!" Lucky shouted. "Our 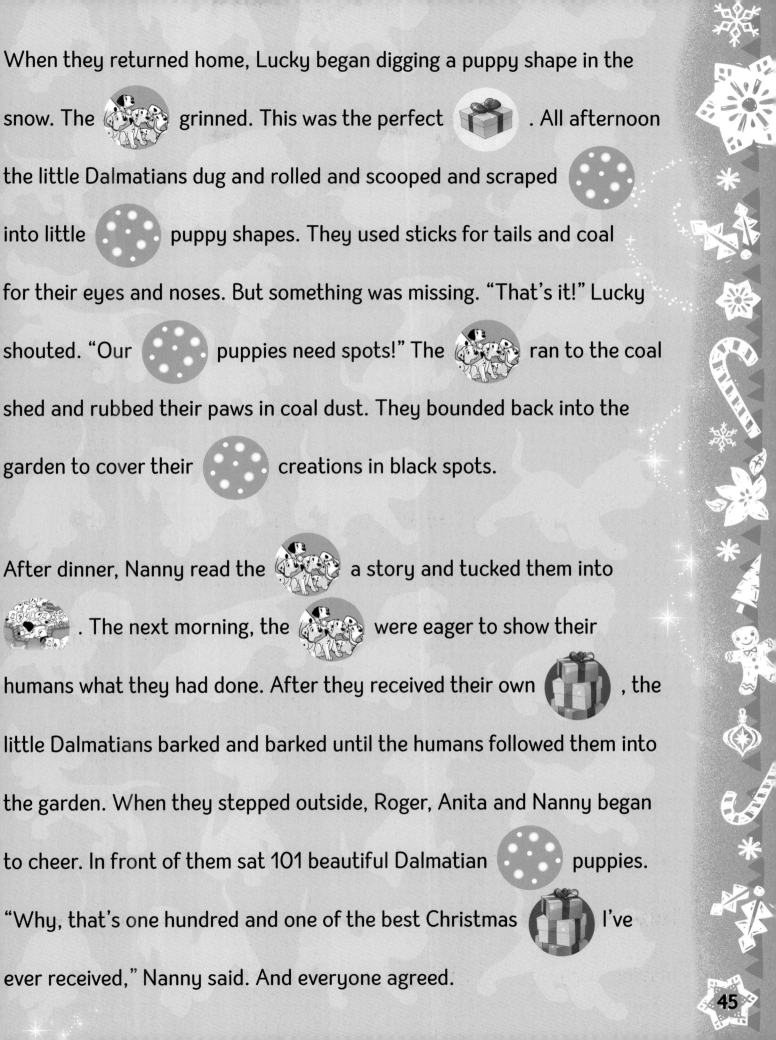 puppies need spots!" The 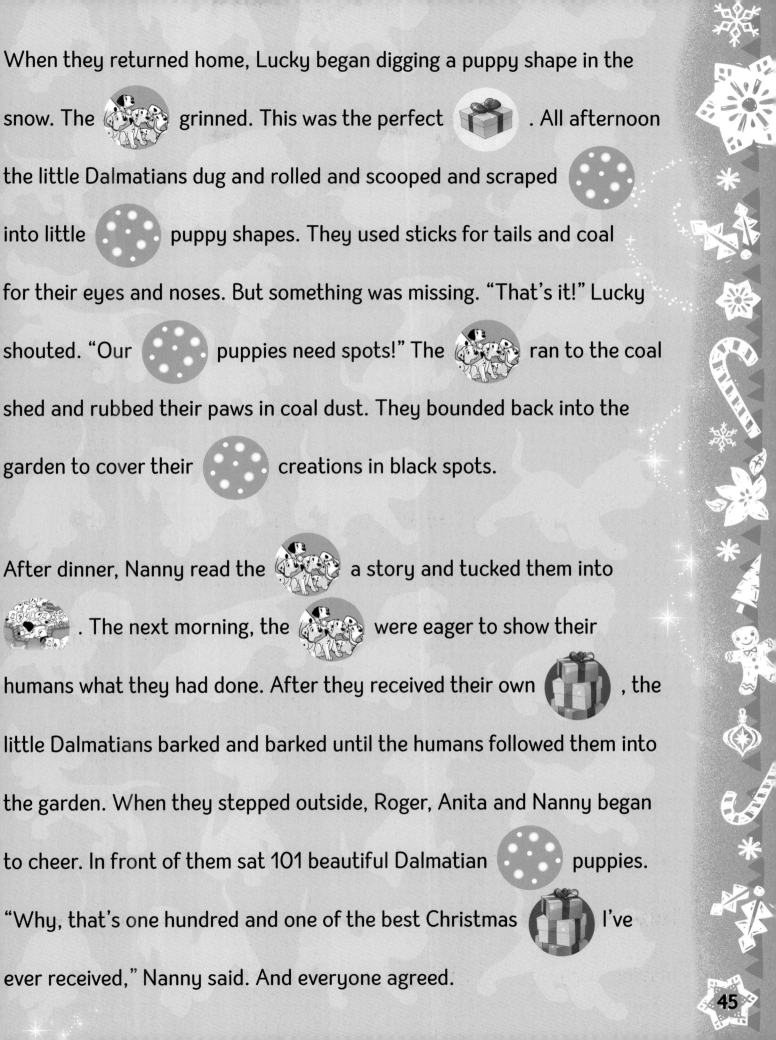 ran to the coal shed and rubbed their paws in coal dust. They bounded back into the garden to cover their 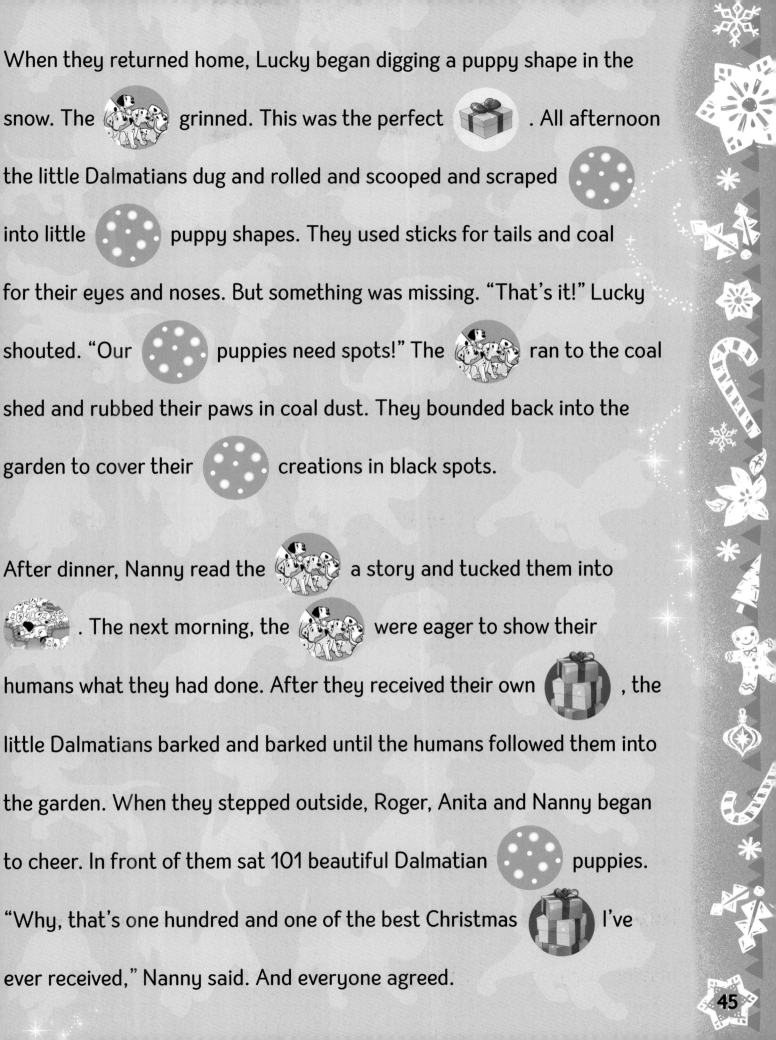 creations in black spots.

After dinner, Nanny read the 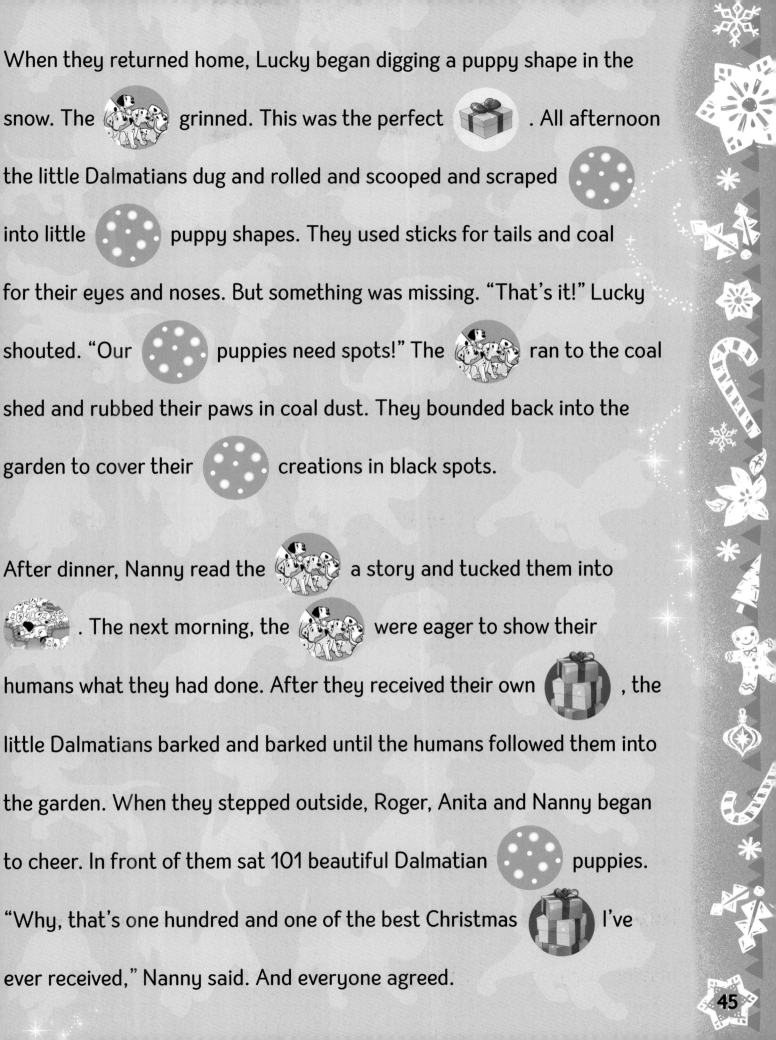 a story and tucked them into 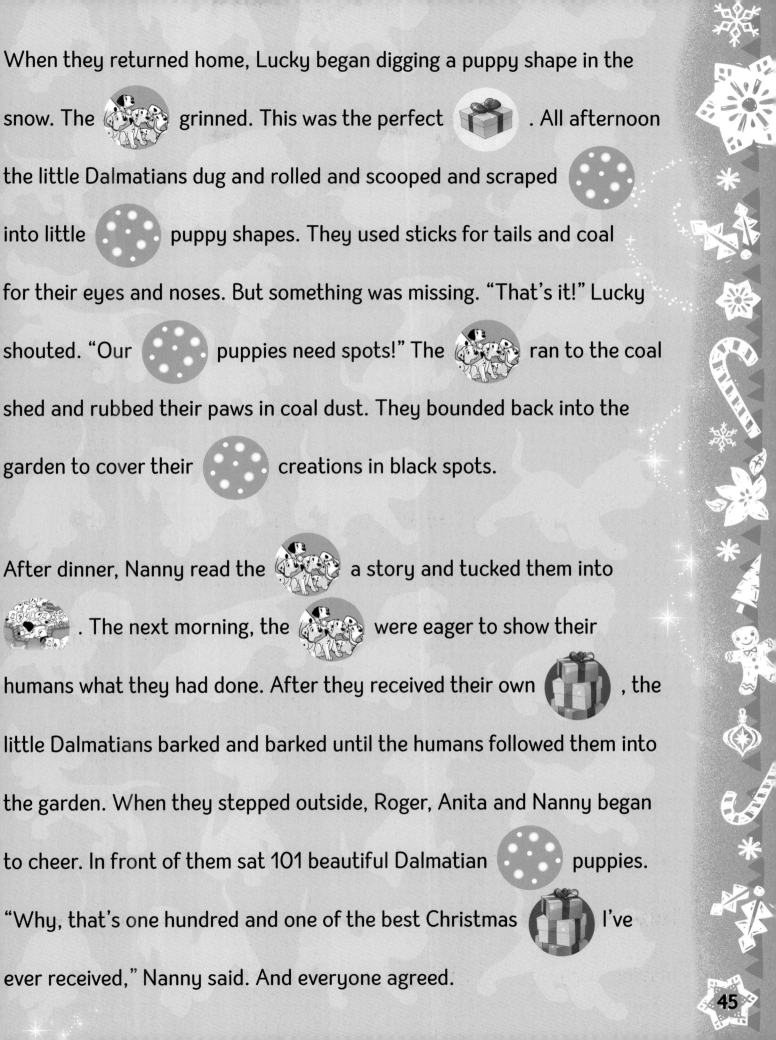 . The next morning, the 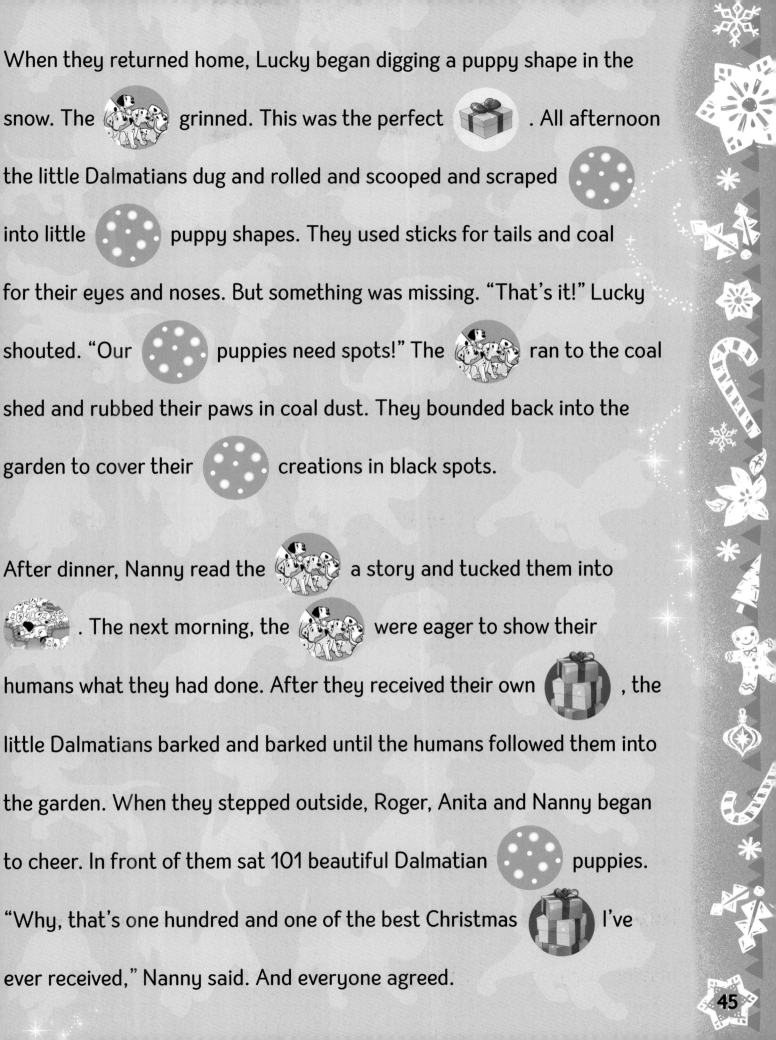 were eager to show their humans what they had done. After they received their own 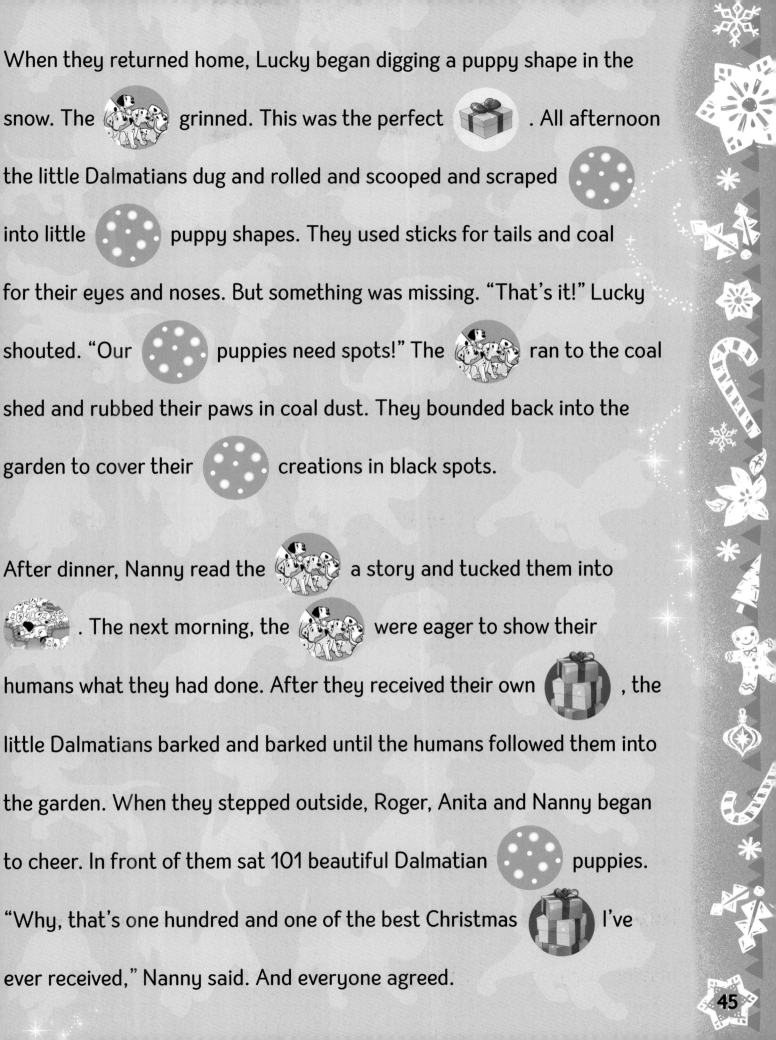 , the little Dalmatians barked and barked until the humans followed them into the garden. When they stepped outside, Roger, Anita and Nanny began to cheer. In front of them sat 101 beautiful Dalmatian 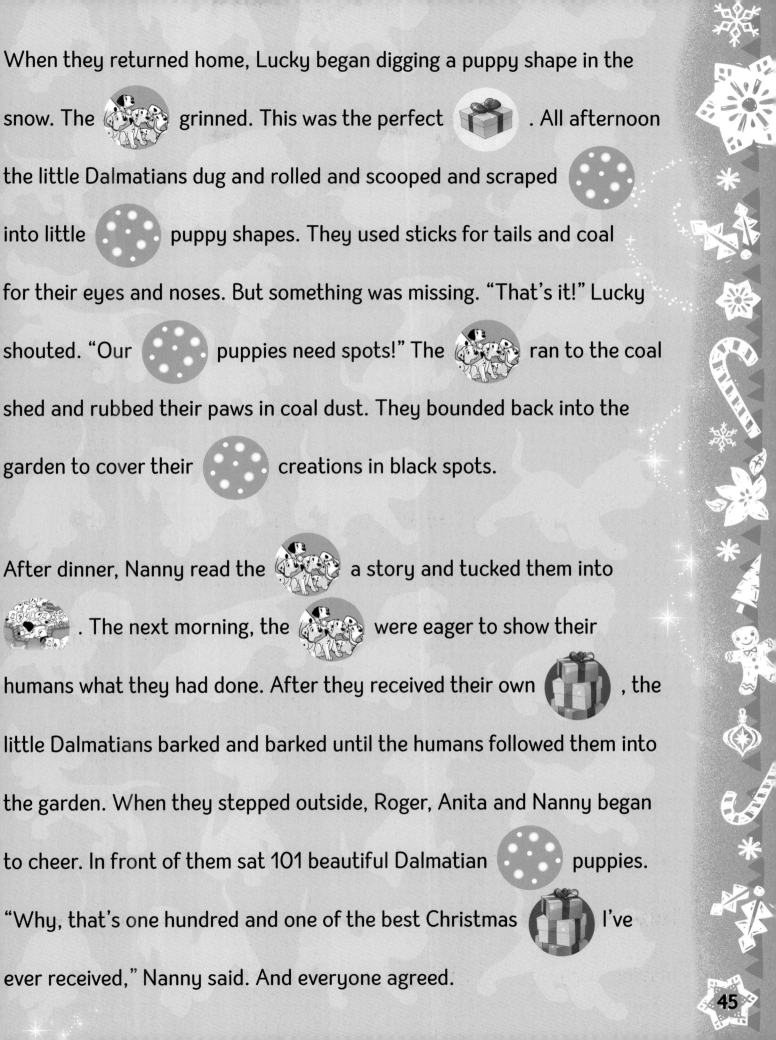 puppies.

"Why, that's one hundred and one of the best Christmas 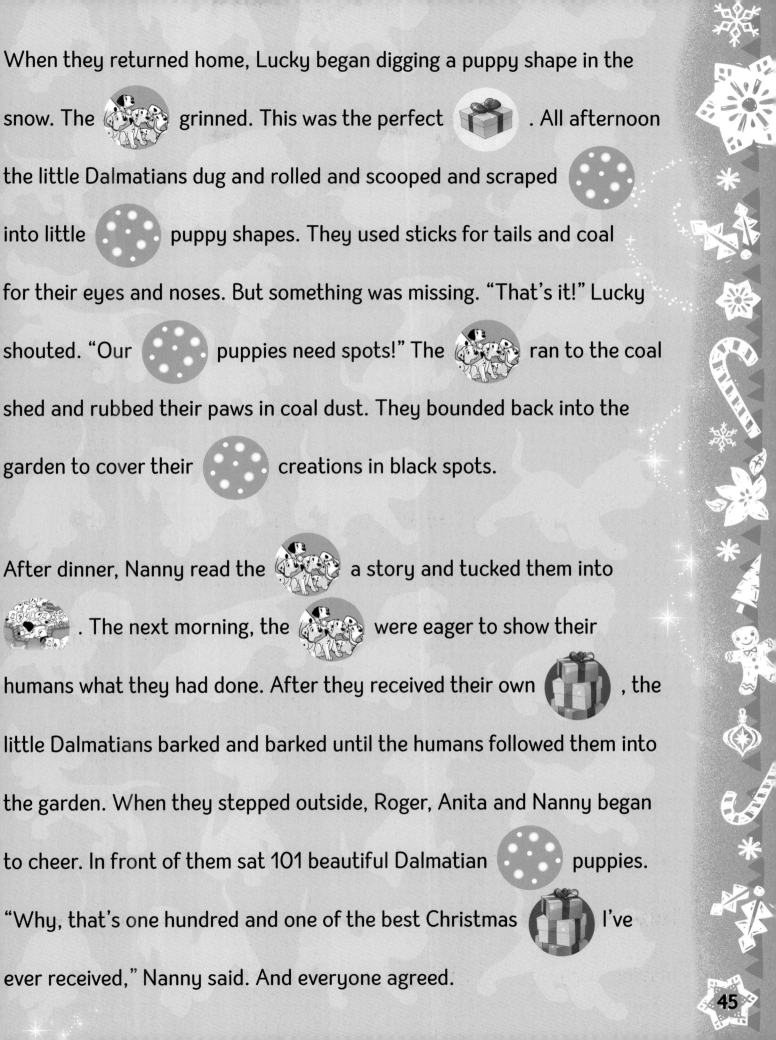 I've ever received," Nanny said. And everyone agreed.

Puppy Problem

Patch is full of mischief. Which picture of the puppy is the odd one out?

46

Present Pursuit

The puppies are ready for presents.
Which path leads to the perfect dog gift?

a

b

c

Jumper Jumble

Pongo and Perdita got woolly Christmas presents this year. Find the missing piece of this picture below.

1

2

3

4

ANSWER: Piece 3 is the missing piece.

Doggy Doodles

The puppies are watching Nanny write out a Christmas shopping list. Can you help by tracing the words below?

tree

star

food

Festive Frogs

Tiana has to finish decorating her Christmas tree but there are so many frogs waiting to be kissed! Help her through the maze avoiding her green friends.

FINISH

START

ANSWER:

Let's Count!

Christmas always goes with a swing at Tiana's Place. Count how many festive items are on this page and colour the right number for each item below.

 **How many** 1 2 3

 **How many** 1 2 3

 **How many** 1 2 3

ANSWER: 2 mittens, 3 gingerbread men and 1 candy cane.

51

Sing Along

Tiana loves singing carols with her friends.

Shining Star

Naveen puts the finishing touches on the tree with a shiny gold star.

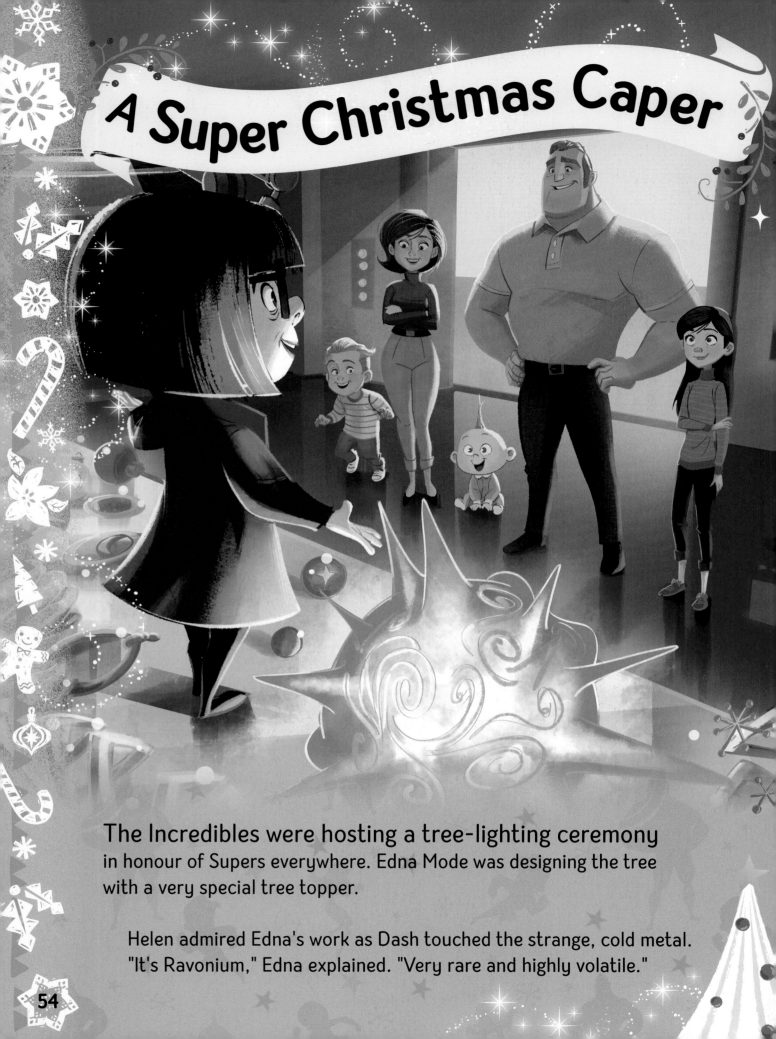

A Super Christmas Caper

The Incredibles were hosting a tree-lighting ceremony
in honour of Supers everywhere. Edna Mode was designing the tree
with a very special tree topper.

Helen admired Edna's work as Dash touched the strange, cold metal.
"It's Ravonium," Edna explained. "Very rare and highly volatile."

The evening of the ceremony, the city was full of Christmas cheer. After some musical performances, the major announced it was time to light the tree. The crowd counted down and the Incredibles pulled the lever. Millions of lights sparked to life all over the towering tree. But everyone gasped as they realised the top was bare – the tree topper was gone!

"What happened? It was just there!" shouted the mayor.

"Thief!" yelled a little girl, pointing at a figure disappearing over the roof of a nearby building.

The Supers would have to act fast if they wanted to catch the thief. They sprang into action!

"There!" shouted Violet, seeing the thief ducking into the gingerbread village. The Supers realised the thief was expert pickpocket Missdirection!

Jack-Jack teleported into the village and lifted one of the gingerbread people. Underneath was Missdirection holding the tree-topper.

Missdirection tried to run, but Jack-Jack stuck to her like glue. Then Dash raced around her with a string of lights, tying her to a candy cane. The Incredibles were so relieved. They couldn't help thinking about the 'highly volatile' nature of Ravonium and what could have happened if it fell into the wrong hands.

The tree topper was put back on the tree and Frozone shot snow flurries high above the city. Mr Incredible hugged his family as they stood with the crowd, admiring the tree. It was a super Christmas, after all.

Questions About the Story

Now you have read this festive *The Incredibles* story, see if you can answer the following questions.

1

What festive job did The Incredibles get asked to do?

a   Light the tree

b   Bake a Christmas cake

c   Wrap some presents

2

What special decoration did Edna make?

a   A garland

b   A tree topper

c   Some tinsel

3

Which Super has the power to make ice with their hands?

a   Elastigirl

b   Dash

c   Frozone

4

Who stole the tree topper?

a   Syndrome

b   Missdirection

c   The Underminer

5

Who found the thief?

a   Violet

b   Mr Incredible

c   Jack-Jack

Meet the Supers!

Mr Incredible

Bob Parr, also known as Mr Incredible, has super strength, enhanced speed and can sense imminent danger. He is also a skilled fighter and is great at making plans to take down the enemy. He is very loyal to his family but loves to spend his time saving the day!

Elastigirl

Bob's wife, Helen, is the infamous Elastigirl. She is extremely cool under pressure and manages to keep her family safe whilst also fighting the baddies. She has superhuman elasticity, which allows her to shapeshift into useful forms such as a parachute or a boat.

Dash

The middle Parr child has superhuman speed. He is so fast he can run over water, has lightning reflexes and is almost untouchable in hand-to-hand combat.

Violet

Helen and Bob's eldest child has the power to become invisible and create nearly indestructible force fields. This makes her a very useful Super as she can protect herself and those around her from attacks.

Jack-Jack

The baby in the family is possibly the most powerful of all the Supers. Some of his powers we know about so far are the ability to become a monster, self-combust, mimic voices, become bigger or smaller, become metal, water or rubber, crawl up walls, duplicate and teleport.

Frozone

Lucius Best is Bob's old friend and partner in the fight against crime. His special power is wielding control over ice. He can use the moisture in the air to create icy platforms, allowing him to move through the air in leaps and bounds. He can also freeze bullets and trap villains in ice.

Race to Christmas

Mr Incredible and Elastigirl have had a busy day of fighting crime and need to get home in time for Christmas with the family. Help them through the maze counting the festive items along the way.

Tick ✔ the items you find. How many?

ANSWER: There are 4 items to find.

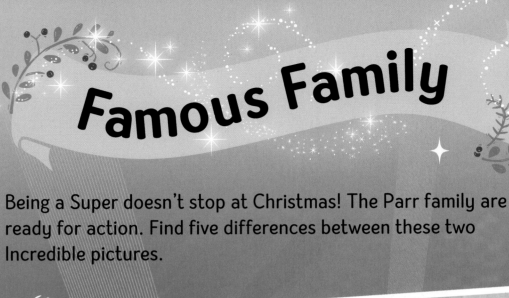

Famous Family

Being a Super doesn't stop at Christmas! The Parr family are ready for action. Find five differences between these two Incredible pictures.

1

64

Colour in a star every time you find a difference.

2

ANSWER: Mr Incredible has a blue collar, the logo is missing from Elastigirl's costume, Dash's hair is the wrong colour, Violet's hair is shorter and Jack-Jack's hair has 2 spikes.

Count and Colour

Ariel is getting the gifts ready for the palace staff.
Count the presents and then colour them in!

ANSWER: There are 7 presents.

Fuzzy Friends

Prince Eric has been asked to invite friends for Christmas dinner. Draw lines to match each character to their name.

a

b

Max

Sebastian

Flounder

c

Scuttle

d

ANSWER: a-Flounder, b-Scuttle, c-Max, d-Sabastian.

Festive Feast

Ariel and Prince Eric are ready for Christmas dinner at the palace!

Shopping Spree

Ariel is trying to get all her Christmas shopping done at the market.